# My Friend Rabbit

ERIC ROHMANN

SCHOLASTIC INC.

New York  Toronto  London  Auckland  Sydney
Mexico City  New Delhi  Hong Kong  Buenos Aires

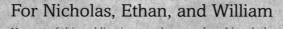

## For Nicholas, Ethan, and William

ISBN 0-439-57683-0

12 11 10 9 8 7 6 5 4 3 2 1          3 4 5 6 7 8/0

Printed in Mexico                                49

First Scholastic printing, September 2003

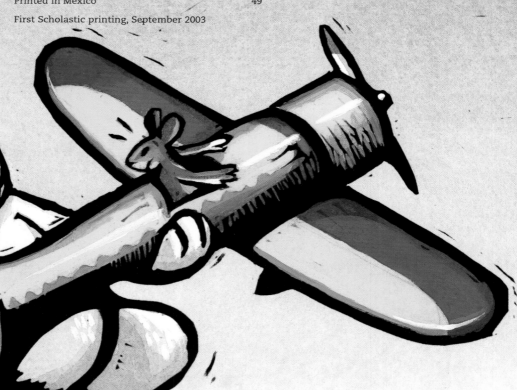

My friend Rabbit means well.
But whatever he does,
wherever he goes,

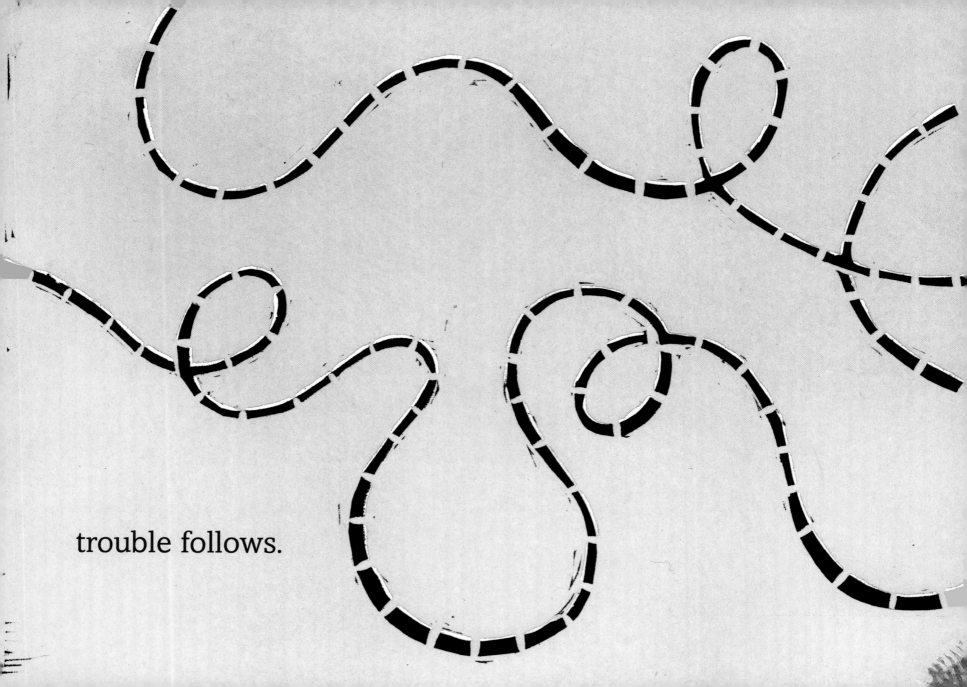

trouble follows.

"Not to worry, Mouse. I've got an idea!"

The plane was
just out of reach.
Rabbit said,
"Not to worry,
Mouse, I've
got an idea."

So Rabbit held Squirrel
and Squirrel held me . . .

but then . . .

The animals
were not
happy.

But Rabbit means well.

And he is my friend.

Even if, whatever he does,

Thank you, Mouse!

Rabbit, stop hugging me!

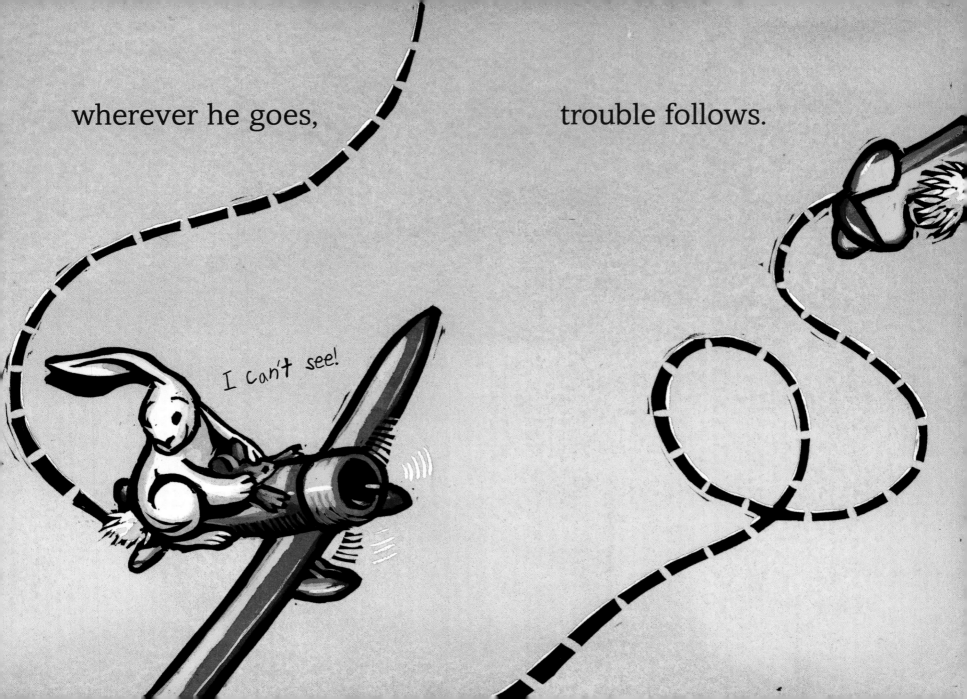

"Not to worry, Mouse,
I've got an idea."